Contents

The contents of this booklet are for general guidance only and should be read in conjunction with your own Local Education Authority Health and Safety Policy. Consult your Local Education Authority Safety Officers and Inspector/Advisers for information about your own Authority's safety policies.

Other safety documents which you are recommended to consult are: "Be Safe!" from ASE, BS 4163 :2000 "Health and safety in workshops of schools and similar establishments".

Remember that Design and Technology activities in primary schools are, for the most part, safe - and great fun! A few simple precautions will enable teachers to work with confidence and provide a rich experience for children.

Introduction — Page : 4

Organising Things — Page : 5

Things that Burn or Explode — Page : 6

Using Chemicals and Substances — Page : 7

Things that are Dusty — Page : 8

Electrical Things — Page : 9

Using Electricity — Page : 10

- Things that Fly — Page :

- Using Food — Page :

- Things that are Heavy — Page : 13

- Things that are Hot — Page : 14

- Using Machines — Page : 15

- Things that are Sharp or Pointed — Page : 16

- Things that are Small — Page : 17

- Things that are Smelly — Page : 18

- Using Computers — Page : 19

- Surfing the Web — Page : 20

- References — Page : 21

Design and Technology describes a way of working in which children investigate a need or respond to an opportunity to make or modify something. They will acquire a range of skills and work in a variety of materials to achieve those aims. Children should be given the opportunity to use: Textiles, Graphics Media, Construction Materials and Food.

These guidance notes are intended to assist those who work with young children to formulate their own school policy concerning Health and Safety for children engaged in practical activities. They do not seek to restrict opportunities for practical activities but to identify the precautions which should be taken to give teachers the confidence to enable the work to proceed with safety.

The guidelines should not be taken as a statement of policy by any Education Authority. Teachers should make sure they have read their own local Health and Safety policy. Consult your authority Safety Officers and Inspector/Advisers, for any clarification on issues raised by these guidelines.

- A balance is required between autonomous learning, through which children may develop their own ideas, and the necessary supervision to ensure safety and success.

- Children will require specific training in safe ways to use potentially dangerous tools and equipment. The best way to achieve this is by clear, confident demonstrations coupled with positive guidance and supervision.

- Schools should ensure that non-teaching assistants, parents, nursery nurses and students are familiar with safe practices. Training should be arranged if needed.

- Teachers should seek advice about good practice, receive training if necessary, and try out a new tool, technique or procedure for themselves to ensure they are aware of potential difficulties or dangers.

- It is important to identify activities which require close supervision and then, through careful lesson planning, ensure that only a manageable number of children is engaged in them at any one time.

- If, in an emergency, the teacher is required to leave the room and there is no responsible adult to oversee the activities, the children who are using potentially dangerous tools or equipment should be told to stop work until the teacher returns. Electrical equipment should be switched off and sharp tools removed.

- Health and Safety training should include aspects of personal hygiene, (eg always washing hands after practical work and before working with food); and good work practices (eg clearing away after an activity)

- Good classroom organisation is essential if children are to learn to look after equipment and replace it after use.

- Children should be made aware also of the possible consequences of their actions on others (eg danger of running in a work area or careless use of tools)

- Relatively few, simple tools are required to produce a wide variety of work. Avoid accepting gifts of tools (eg saws, chisels, kitchen knives) from well intentioned parents and others, as these are often unsuitable for Design and Technology in schools.

- All teachers should know what procedure to follow in the event of an emergency. Teachers should refer to their local authority Health and Safety policy document.

Good organisation of tools and equipment is essential both for safe working and to enable children to accept some responsibility for their own learning.

Children should be taught to take care of tools and equipment, work systematically and to clear away afterwards.

- There should be a clear distinction between equipment which is for general use, that which can only be used under direct supervision, and that which is for teacher use only.

- Tools and equipment for general use by children, are best stored on shadow boards or mobile trolleys with each tool space indicated.

- Store materials which children require in such a way that easy and safe access is possible (e.g. do not fix wall mounted tool-boards above children's eye level).

- Avoid using glass jars to store hardware items.

- Large, clear, flat surfaces are most suitable for practical work (e.g. several tables together) with clear spaces around them.

- Encourage children to keep work surfaces clear both during and after working.

- Ensure that surfaces used for food preparation are kept clean.

- Avoid trailing extension leads across the floor where they can trip people up.

- Ensure that there is a good level of both artificial and natural light.

- Teachers and supervising adults should understand the local authority/school arrangements for First Aid; know where the First Aid facilities are located; and the person responsible for First Aid within the school. The contents of the First Aid box or cabinet should be checked and replenished as necessary.

First Aid Advice

Minimum contents of the First Aid cabinet:

Guidance card; 20 individually wrapped sterile & adhesive dressings; 2 sterile eye pads; 6 triangular bandages; 6 medium, 2 large and 3 extra large unmedicated sterile dressings; 6 safety pins.

Before any activity with naked flames, ensure that appropriate fire extinguishers are available.

Teachers should take care to control the use and ensure the security of fuels and matches as well as being alert to hazards directly associated with heating.

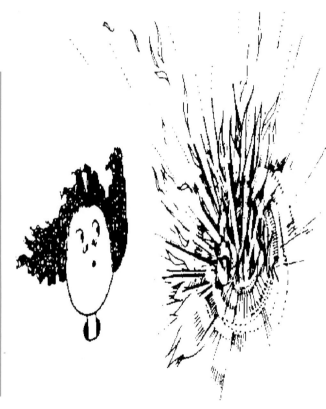

- Teachers should be able to identify flammable liquids and ensure that the quantity kept is as small as is reasonably practicable. Check local authority requirements regarding the use of fire resistant cabinets or containers to store flammable materials.

- Do not use any solvent-based paints or adhesives near naked flames.

- Do not attempt to puncture, burn or incinerate aerosol cans. Dispose of them immediately they become empty.

- Launch hot air balloons from a hair dryer or fan heater. Do not allow them to fly untethered with their own naked flame heat source.

- No mains electrical equipment should be used near water (e.g. mains electric hair dryers or fan heaters to power model boats).

- Rechargeable batteries may explode if immersed in water.

- Equipment such as hot air paint strippers can burn and should be used only by the teacher.

- Do not use methylated spirit burners, oil stoves (eg paraffin, diesel) including pressure stoves (Primus), or gas burners mounted on gas cylinders. They can spill and cause a fire.

- Do not use solid fuels, intended for picnic stoves for example, as they usually contain poisonous chemicals e.g. metaldehyde or hexamine.

- Candles, Calorettes, Night Lights, and small quantities of hot water are recommended sources of heat.

- The area around a naked flame should be cleared of paper and anything easily ignitable.

First Aid Advice

Clothing on Fire:

Speed is important. Better to lower the victim to the ground to smother the flames than to spend time searching for a blanket.

Keep flames away from the face.

Several common chemicals and household substances have uses in Design and Technology. Teachers should use them confidently but be aware of potential hazards. Always follow the manufacturer's instructions and the Local Education Authority COSHH guidelines.

Children should know that substances are not necessarily safe simply because they can be bought from a shop!

- The UK Control of Substances Hazardous to Health Regulations 1999, requires employers to assess the substances hazardous to health, the risk involved in their use, and the precautions which need to be taken. Teachers should consult their local authority COSHH guidelines.

- A substance is only potentially hazardous: the risk it presents will depend partly on this but also on how it is used and length of exposure (e.g. photocopying produces hazardous fumes but little appreciable risk in normal use).

- The COSHH regulations apply also to any substances which we produce as a result of a process or activity (e.g. sanding dust, fumes from a polystyrene cutter).

- Having assessed that there is a risk, the teacher must follow the local authority procedure. In drawing up the COSHH assessment, the local authority would have considered the following:

  (a) whether or not the product/substance should be discontinued;

  (b) the location of an alternative, less hazardous substance;

  (c) identification of procedures for safe use eg. the creation of dust - use a dust extractor and ensure the room is well ventilated.

  (d) adoption of suitable personal protection (e.g. wear a face mask or eye protection)

- Be aware of the warning symbols used on products. The most likely ones are those used to classify substances as: Flammable, Harmful, Irritant or Corrosive.

First Aid Advice

Consult a doctor if a child suffers headaches, fainting or vomiting as a result of exposure to a substance, stating the substance involved.

Children who faint should be laid on their backs with their legs in the air.

The amount of dust created in a primary classroom is unlikely to present a serious health risk but the LEA COSHH assessments should be checked. Care must be taken when sanding or shaping materials (e.g. wood, metals, plastics, plaster and ceramics).

All dust created must be removed using a damp cloth or vacuum cleaner rather than by brushing.

- Avoid the creation of unnecessary dust.

- Plastics, and metals such as aluminium, should be smoothed using "wet or dry" abrasive papers with water to avoid dust.

- Be aware of the danger of sawdust or splinters being blown into the eyes when working with wood.

- The dust from hardwoods, softwoods and some manufactured boards, such as Medium Density Fibreboard (MDF), can be hazardous therefore avoid excessive sanding and remove any dust using a damp cloth.

- Avoid all contact with asbestos.

- Very young children can easily scratch their eyes with sand from the sand tray and must not be left, even for a short while, to play unattended with sand or water.

- Hot wire cutters must be used only in well ventilated conditions to shape expanded polystyrene (i.e. as used to make ceiling tiles). The cutting wire should be just hot enough to cut the polystyrene without generating too much smoke. Do not sand polystyrene.

- Equipment used when glazing ceramics should be washed when still wet. Glazes containing over 5% soluble lead should not be used at all in schools.

- Ground flint should not be used for dusting kiln furniture or making a bat wash. Wherever possible, flint should be kept in either slop or paste form.

- Do not prepare food where pottery activities are carried out or where there is likely to be dust e.g. from wood, metals, plastics, or plaster.

First Aid Advice

Eye problems:

Disposable eye irrigation bottles, containing water, are recommended and they should be discarded after use.

Tap water may be used if nothing else is available.

Although children will generally not need to handle mains electrical equipment at school, they should be taught how to plug it in and use it safely. They should be taught never to experiment with mains electricity. Warn them of electrical dangers in the home.

Local Education Authority policy, incorporating the "Electricity at Work Regulations 1989", should be checked. If in doubt you should consult your local authority Safety Officers and Inspector/Advisers.

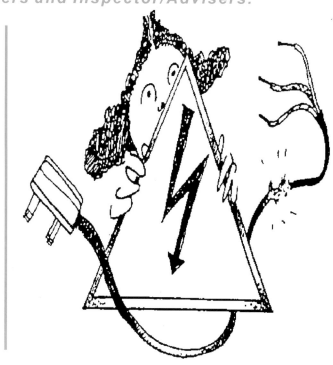

- Mains electric equipment can be made safer to use by fitting a Residual Current Device (RCD). This can be installed in an easily accessible position, to serve all the sockets in a room, or as plug tops fitted to individual pieces of equipment.

- All portable electrical equipment should be checked on a regular basis. Teachers should check visually all mains equipment for faulty plugs or leads whenever it is used.

- Children should be taught to switch off at the wall socket before plugging in or unplugging mains equipment. "Shatterproof" type plug tops, with shrouded pins are recommended.

- Never use mains electrical equipment near water and always have RCD protection if used outdoors.

- Plug tops should be wired by a competent adult. Check for correct colour coding - brown goes to "live"; blue to "neutral"; green and yellow striped is earth. Ensure that there exists at least single insulation right up to the terminal and that the outer coverings are securely gripped by the cable clamp.

- To check correct fuse size divide Watts by Volts eg. 500 W (0.5 kW) appliance divided by nominal mains voltage of 250V gives a fuse size of 2 Amps only. 3 Amp or 5 Amp fuses will be suitable for most appliances in primary schools. Plugs often have 13A fuses fitted when purchased, which should be changed.

- Extension leads and leads from portable equipment should be fully extended when in use to avoid overheating. Where appropriate follow the manufacturers' instructions.

- Mains powered soldering irons should have heat resistant silicone rubber cable and RCD plug tops fitted. Use low voltage soldering irons where possible.

First Aid Advice

Electricity can kill!
In case of electric shock, ensure power is off, resuscitate if required. Any resulting burns should always be seen by a doctor.
Posters showing what to do in case of electric shock should be prominently displayed.

Electrical work using torch batteries is safe because the voltages involved are low.

There is a danger however, that pupils might try to continue their work at home using the mains.

It is important to stress to pupils that playing with mains sockets is very dangerous and can be fatal!

- Dry batteries are safest to use. It is not possible to get an electric shock unless a great many of them are joined together.

- Some modern torch batteries contain harmful chemicals and so should not be cut open (e.g. Alkaline batteries can become hot and should not be punctured or used by young children—see reference to CLEAPSS guide L1112)

- Dry batteries cannot be recharged and no attempt should be made to do so. Never put them in an oven in a mistaken attempt to rejuvenate them.

- Old batteries should be discarded safely as they often leak their contents.

- Tiny batteries as used in watches are not suitable for use in primary schools.

- Wires and battery cases can get very hot if batteries are allowed to discharge too quickly. They should be stored so that their terminals cannot touch.

- Rechargeable batteries can be used over and over again but only by older children using battery powered equipment (e.g. for Lego in which they are correctly encased). They should not be used for circuit work. High capacity rechargeable batteries and unknown makes are best avoided.

- Rechargeable batteries may explode if dropped in water.

- Always supervise recharging using only a charger designed for the type of battery being used.

- Car batteries and accumulators are not appropriate for use with young children.

- Low voltage power supplies can be a most useful source of electrical energy but their use should be restricted to older children. All power supplies should meet UK regulations and standards. Equipment from unknown suppliers should always be regarded with suspicion.

First Aid Advice

Burns should be cooled with water, acid burns should be flooded with water for 10 to 15 mins. Consult a doctor.
If any chemicals are swallowed, dilute with water or milk, do not induce vomiting, seek immediate medical aid.

Topics on flight can lead to the exciting activities associated with kites, rockets, hot air balloons and aeroplanes. These are relatively safe activities, provided they are properly supervised, but there are dangers from over-head power lines, from fuels, from flying too close to roads or an airport.

Be aware also of the dangers from testing model catapults, mangonels and ballistas.

- The Civil Aviation Authority, under the powers of the Air Navigation Orders 1980, has issued the following article regarding the flying of kites, balloons and airships:

  67 (1)   Within the United Kingdom -

  (a) a captive balloon or kite shall not be flown at a height of more than 60 metres above the ground level or within 60 metres of any vessel, vehicle or structure

  (d) a kite shall not be flown within 5km of an aerodrome;

- Wear gloves when flying larger kites in strong winds: nylon lines can give painful friction burns.

- Never fly kites close to power lines

- Hot air balloons are best filled using hair driers: they can be flown indoors.

- Never free fly a hot air balloon using burning fuel.

- In the interest of hygiene, use balloon pumps to blow up party balloons.

- Launch water rockets away from spectators and be aware of the danger presented by pointed nose cones.

- Always follow the manufacturer's instructions when launching commercially available solid fuel rockets or compressed air powered rockets such as those available through the Technology Enhancement Project (www.tep.org.uk)

- Never experiment with home made fuels.

- Test model catapults, ballistas and mangonels with care; use projectiles that are safe (i.e. not ball bearings or sharp objects), direct them away from spectators.

First Aid Advice

Friction burns should be treated as cuts and grazes.

Stop bleeding from cuts, apply clean dressing.

Resuscitate in case of electric shock.

The following relates to the preparation of food for human consumption but the use of food in Design and Technology is not limited to this. An appreciation of the importance of cleanliness and personal hygiene is essential in topics involving food.

Before starting any work with food, children should tie back long hair, wash their hands with soap and water, and cover any cuts or scratches on the hands with waterproof dressings.

- Encourage children to wear clean aprons which are kept specifically for working with food, use oven gloves and heat proof mats.

- Ensure that children re-wash their hands after breaks and visits to the toilet.

- Very young children will put their fingers in their mouth so clean water trays at regular intervals and keep sand trays fresh by washing sand occasionally in a mild bleach solution, drying off thoroughly before use.

- Cover table surfaces to be used for food preparation with a clean plastic sheet and clean with disinfecting solution (eg Milton or Detox) before use.

- Food preparation equipment, including cutlery, should be cleaned and dried before being stored. Store separately and use only for food preparation. Use separate equipment for preparation of animal food.

- Ovens used for cooking food should not be used for other purposes (eg heating plastics).

- Follow manufacturer's instructions when siting and using a microwave oven.

- Site cookers and ovens well away from flammable materials and be aware of dangers associated with the movements of children (e.g. do not leave pan handles projecting over the edge of the cooker)

- Food should not normally be stored overnight in school but, if small quantities are kept, they should be in labelled, rodent proof containers. Be aware that some children may be allergic to some foods. Carefully dispose of waste using polythene bags.

- If refrigerators are used to store food, they should be clean and set to between 2 and 5 deg C : freezers should be set to minus 18 deg C or less.

- A special washing up bowl should be set aside for washing food implements. Make sure that dish cloths and tea towels are washed regularly.

- Know what to do in case of fire. Avoid activities involving boiling sugar or oil.

First Aid Advice

If poisoning is suspected, refer to doctor with a sample of the substance. Do not try to induce vomiting.
Minor burns and scalds should be cooled under gently running water for 10 to 15 mins. Do not apply creams or ointments.

Care must be taken not to leave heavy objects near the edges of tables where they can be knocked off on to someone's foot.

Pupils must never be permitted to attempt to lift loads beyond their own physical capabilities.

Pupils should be taught the safe rules for lifting.

- Do not store materials, for pupil use, above head height. Do not place them where pupils may be tempted to stand on things in an attempt to reach them.

- Use sand poured into a plastics bucket or water in plastic bottles to test bridges etc. Do not use bricks or heavy metal weights with sharp corners.

- If pupils are to lift loads as part of a class activity, they should do so only under supervision and wear substantial footwear. Open toed sandals or plimsolls are not acceptable.

- Pupils should wear gloves if they need to handle heavy, sharp cornered objects such as house bricks.

RULES FOR LIFTING:

- *Stand with feet apart (but not wider than your hips) and positioned so that one foot is behind and the other alongside the object, pointing in the direction of movement after lifting.*

- *Bend your knees, not your back.*

- *Get a firm grip with the whole hand: not just the finger tips.*

- *Keep your back straight, your chin tucked in and lift by straightening your legs.*

- *Keep the load close to your body.*

- *Always be able to see over the top of a load.*

- *Get help opening doors.*

- *Avoid trapping your fingers when releasing the load.*

First Aid Advice

Cool trapped fingers with water to relieve pain and swelling,

Refer to a doctor if a fracture or other damage is suspected.

Sources of heat such as gas rings, hot plates, kettles, cookers, soldering irons and hot glue guns should be placed out of reach and used only by older, responsible children after instruction and under close supervision.

If there is no tap in the room, a container of cold water should always be available to deal with burns and scalds.

- Supervise pupils with particular care when they are heating things.

- Give appropriate instructions and check that cautions are understood and observed.

- Point out to children that things can be hot even when they don't appear so.

- Test if something is still hot by placing a hand above it rather than by touching.

- If hot water is required, use only the minimum needed at the lowest possible temperature. Use a safe, closed topped container (e.g. a kettle) if you must carry hot water about.

- Use hot glue guns and soldering irons over a piece of hardboard, or similar place mat to avoid damage to the furniture. Glue guns should be placed on stands in readiness to be used.

- Low temperature glue guns are available, which are safer for children to use: note also that they will glue expanded polystyrene.

- Consult with your local authority advisers or safety officers regarding who may use a glue gun (e.g. only older children are permitted to use them in several local authorities).

- Pottery kilns should comply with local authority regulations regarding their location and the provision of interlocks, safety guards and fume extraction. Never use pottery kilns for other purposes.

First Aid Advice

Burns and Scalds:

As quickly as possible, cool the affected area in cold water, preferably running, for at least ten minutes. Carefully remove any jewellery, dress with "Cling Film" or other light, non-fluffy material. Treat for shock and refer to a doctor if more than the size of the casualty's hand.

There is very little need for any powered equipment for Design and Technology in primary schools.

You are strongly advised not to bring into school any power tools from home or to accept them as gifts to school.

If power tools are to be used, a range of low voltage equipment is available and is preferred (eg small model maker's drilling machine) - note that you should check that power tools of any kind are permitted by your Local Education Authority.

- Always consult your local authority Inspector/Adviser before purchasing any powered equipment.

- Check with your local authority Inspector/Adviser or Safety Officer that children are permitted to use power tools and in what circumstances.

- Eye and hair protection should be used when using power tools. Eye protection should be to the BS 2092 specification. Face shields are preferred to goggles.

- Never let more than one pupil at a time use a power tool or machine. Do not let children crowd near a machine in use.

- All portable electrical equipment should be fitted with RCD plug tops and , where appropriate, securely mounted on to a base board which can be clamped to the table top.

- Food mixers should be cleaned by the teacher or other adult.

- Make sure the work is securely held when using powered equipment.

- If, as in a specialist design and technology area, the classroom is equipped with an emergency stop system, all power equipment with moving parts should normally be fitted with a no-volt overload switch to prevent its restarting when the power is switched back on. Teachers should refer to their local authority advisers or safety officers for further guidance.

First Aid Advice

Eye injuries should be bathed, eye wash bottles are available: do not use eye baths.

If high velocity particles are suspected, refer to doctor or a hospital even though no particle can be seen.

The use of sharp edge tools such as wood chisels and large kitchen knives should be avoided in primary schools.

Any sharp edge tools which are used should be stored separately to be issued at teacher's discretion and used under direct supervision.

- Craft knives should only be used by older children under direct supervision. Use knives with a safety rule and on a cutting mat. Teach children to keep their fingers behind the cutting edge of sharp tools.

- Sharp pointed scissors are not recommended for use with very young children and reception classes. Be aware also of the danger of sharp pointed pencils, compasses points and paint brush ends. Avoid sharpening pencils at both ends.

- Teach children how to hold work securely when sawing it. A small clamp-on vice is suitable but most pupils can also use a small bench hook successfully with junior hacksaws. A 'G' cramp can also be used. The work should always be fixed in a vice when using a coping saw.

- Use saws with disposable blades to avoid maintenance problems e.g. junior hacksaw, joiner's precision mitre saw, coping saw. Because of their smaller teeth, metal cutting blades in junior hacksaws are safest for use with young children and are efficient even when sawing wood and plastics. Make sure the teeth are pointing forwards.

- Saws and knives with sharp blades are safer than those with blunt ones, when used correctly, because they take less force to push them through the material.

- Bend over the end of lengths of stiff wire to avoid danger to eyes.

- Keep hands behind the cutting edge of lino tools and push away from the body. Use a bench hook to support the work.

- Store needles in pads which can easily be checked visually.

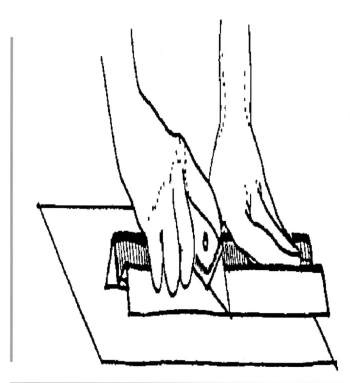

First Aid Advice

Do not use creams or ointments when treating cuts and minor wounds.

Refer stab wounds to a medical practitioner.

Several small objects are commonly used in technology work. Teachers should be aware of dangers associated with very young children placing small objects into their mouths.

There is a danger of small fragments of materials being blown into eyes. Splinters of some materials can produce adverse reactions.

- The removable tops from certain pens are particularly dangerous if swallowed: they can restrict the airways and prevent a child from breathing. Select only those pens with tops designed to obviate this danger (e.g. pen caps with holes in the top).

- Never allow children to bang together hammer heads. The steel used is very hard and splinters can fly off at great speed. There is a considerable danger that one of these splinters could damage eyes. Always check that the hammer head is correctly secured to the shaft.

- Splinters from certain hardwoods (eg Meranti) can cause a skin reaction. Balsa is less hazardous as is Jelutong and pine which have the added advantage of being harvested from sustainable forests.

- Always wrap up any broken glass in newspaper before disposing of it and label the package clearly. Never put unwrapped broken glass in a bin which may be cleared by an unsuspecting person. Good practice is to remove it to a metal dustbin outside.

- Carefully supervise the storage and distribution of drawing pins, staples, needles and mapping pins etc. Pins should not be used as an anchor point for stretched elastic bands.

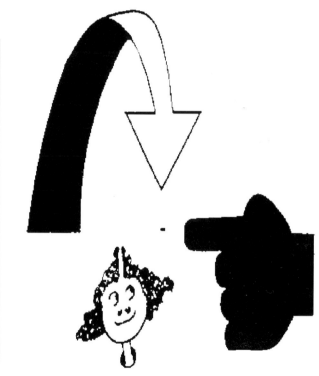

First Aid Advice

In the event of choking, clear any obstruction from the mouth, lean casualty forward and give five thumps on the back. Repeat if necessary.

Splinters should be removed carefully with tweezers: do not 'dig' to remove them.

Glues and paints based on solvents should always be avoided where possible and, if used, do so in small quantities in well ventilated conditions. Only a few children at a time should be using them, preferably near an open window and under close supervision. Use alternative, water based glues and paints when possible.

Teachers should always check their Local Education Authority COSHH assessments to determine safe procedures.

- Always check that you understand the hazard warning symbols on any containers. Follow manufacturers' instructions and take recommended precautions.

- Some cleaning agents can produce harmful vapours.

- Avoid solvent based adhesives. Safer, water based versions are available which work just as well.

- Working in glass fibre is not suitable for work with young children.

- Expanded polystyrene (i.e. as used to make ceiling tiles) is best cut using hot wire cutters to avoid harmful dust, but use near an open window and do not have more than one or two operating at the same time.

- The cutting wire should be just hot enough to cut the polystyrene without generating too much smoke. It is these fumes which can cause headaches.

- Never use hot wire cutters for cutting polyurethane foam. (i.e. as sold for use with glass fibre kits or in upholstery).

- The fumes from solvent or spirit based felt tip pens can cause headaches so they too should be used only sparingly in well ventilated conditions.

- Metallic gold and silver pens are best avoided and not used at all with very young children.

- Cans of spray paints should be used with care and preferably outdoors or in purpose made spray booths. Cellulose paints as used for car body work are generally unsuitable.

- The fumes produced by the hot flux when soldering can cause headaches.

- Indiscriminate heating of certain plastics can produce harmful fumes.

- Sniff tests of spices should be done through muslin.

First Aid Advice

In the event of fainting or dizziness refer to a medical practitioner stating the substance which caused it.

Computers can be used extensively to enhance designing and making and to give children experience of control and systems.

Health and Safety regulations concerning use of computers tend to be directed towards administrative staff and computer operatives who spend a large part of their working days at a computer workstation.

There are, nonetheless, some common - sense precautions which teachers should be aware of to ensure that children have a safe and comfortable working environment.

- A regular visual inspection of all mains electrical equipment is essential, especially if computers are moved about on trolleys.

- Do not use more than one double socket adaptor onto an existing wall socket outlet. Ensure extension leads are always fully unwound to prevent over-heating. Avoid trailing leads which children could trip over.

- Children should be taught the dangers associated with plugging in and unplugging mains electrical equipment and only older children allowed to do it.

- Children should take a break from computers every 20 mins. to 30 mins. and be encouraged to stretch their legs and relax their eyes by looking at distant objects.

- The work surface should be large enough to leave adequate space around the keyboard and monitor to allow the user to change position and vary movements.

- The computer screen should be positioned to give a comfortable viewing position including for two children when computers are shared.

- Make sure children know how to adjust the screen for brightness and contrast and position monitors to avoid glare from lights or windows.

- Position monitors such that no child sits within one metre of the back or side of a monitor to minimise any slight radiation risks (World Health Organisation recommendation)

First Aid Advice

Excessive use of computers can lead to eye strain, neck-ache or headaches. Do not administer drugs but allow time for rest away from the screen. Prevention by good positioning and screen setting is better than cure.

The millions of web sites on the Internet can be a rich source of ideas and information for Design and Technology. Facilities also exist to allow designs to be exchanged, parts to be manufactured on equipment in other places and for children to 'ask an expert'. The Internet is not controlled by any particular organisation however and the quality and validity of any information cannot be guaranteed.

In addition, there are well-publicised dangers to children associated with internet use. Schools have always helped learners cope with such matters by providing clear support and guidance. The Internet is no exception and its educational benefits outweigh the possible dangers. (see http://www.safety.ngfl.gov.uk)

- Schools have a responsibility to filter out Internet access to undesirable materials both at school and when web access forms part of home-school links. This may be provided by the school Internet Service Provider (ISP) or can be added at the workstation using suitable software.

- At school, Pupils should access the internet in well supervised areas with monitors on open display.

- Schools should also check that emails are scanned for viruses and ensure there is virus protection software on all workstations.

- Email addresses should be restricted to mailboxes for a whole class or subject and not individualised to children unless circulation is restricted to an internal email system.

- School web pages should not include photographs of children unless they are in a group such that individual identification is not possible, unnamed, and permission is sought from parents.

- Use of 'chat' rooms should be restricted to moderated educational chat rooms (eg http://www.gridclub.com) and not used unsupervised.

Be WebSafe—adapted from **NetSmart Rules** by the charity NCH (see www.nchafc.org.uk/internet/default.asp)

- *Never tell anyone you meet on the internet your home address, your telephone number or your school's name, unless your parent, carer or teacher specifically gives you permission.*
- *Never send anyone your picture, credit card or bank details, without first checking with your parent ,carer or teacher.*
- *Never arrange to meet anyone unless your parent or carer goes with you and you meet in a public place. People you contact online are not always who they seem, even people who become pen friends or 'keypals'. People don't always tell the truth online – no one can see them.*
- *Never open attachments to e-mails unless they come from someone you already know and trust. They could contain viruses or other programmes which would destroy all the information and software on your computer.*
- *Never respond to nasty or suggestive messages. Always tell your parent or carer if you get such messages or if you see rude pictures while online and report them to your Internet Service Provider.*
- *Always keep your password to yourself, do not share it with anyone.*
- *Always check with your parent or carer that it is ok to be in a chat room and always be very careful in chat rooms. Even if a chat room says it is only for children, there's no way at the moment to tell if everyone there really is a child. It might be an adult or an older child trying to trick you. Always get out of a chat room if someone says or writes something which makes you feel uncomfortable or worried. Make sure you tell your parent or carer.*
- *Always be yourself and do not pretend to be anyone or anything you are not.*
- *Always stay away from sites that say they are for people over 18 only. The warnings are there to protect you*

*This booklet gives a brief indication only of the safety issues concerned with Design and Technology in primary schools. A companion volume **Be Safe**, relating to primary school Science and Technology activities, is also available. **Be Safe** is published by th e Association for Science Education and can be ordered from their address given below.*

The following references have been used to compile this text and should be consulted if further information is required. Reference should be made also to the Health and Safety Executive, your Local Education Authority Safety Officers and Inspector/Advisers

BIBLIOGRAPHY:

- Health and Safety in Workshops of Schools and Similar Establishments: *BS 4163(1984) - from HMSO*
- Electrical Safety in Schools (Electricity atWork Regulations 1989) Guidance Note GS23 (Electrical Safety) revised 1990: *Health and Safety Executive*
- COSHH: Guidance for Schools: *Health and Safety Executive*
- Be Safe!: *Association for Science Education*
- First Aid Manual: *St. John's Ambulance Ass.*
- Arrangements for First Aid Provision in Schools and Colleges: *DES Guidance Note 1987*
- Tools: *by R. Jones:Commotion Publishing (081 804 1378)*
- CLEAPSS publications including:
  - L5p Safe Use of Household and other Chemicals (1999)
  - L86p Electrical Safety (1985)
  - L111 Tools and Techniques
  - GLU Glues and Adhesives (2000)
  - L112 Batteries etc - Which to Buy (1993)

USEFUL ADDRESSES:

National Association of Advisers and Inspectors in Design and Technology (www.naaaidt.org.uk)
c/o DATA
16 Wellesbourne House
Walton Road
Wellesbourne
Warwickshire
CV35 9JB

The Association for Science Education (www.ase.org.uk)
College Lane
Hatfield
Hertfordshire
AL10 9AA

CLEAPSS (www.cleapss.org.uk)
School Science Service
Brunel University
Uxbridge
UB8 3PH

Health and Safety Executive inspectors are based in offices that are organised into divisions.
Offices are open 9 am to 5 pm,   Monday to Friday.
Full contact details are available from the HSE web site (www.hse.gov.uk/contact/index.htm)

WALES & WEST DIVISION

Covers Wales and the unitary authorities of Cornwall, Devon, Somerset, North West Somerset, Bath and North East Somerset, Bristol, South Gloucestershire, Gloucestershire, Hereford & Worcester, Shropshire and Staffordshire.

HOME COUNTIES DIVISION

Covers the counties of Bedfordshire, Berkshire, Buckinghamshire, Cambridgeshire, Dorset, Essex (except London Boroughs in Essex), Hampshire, Hertfordshire, Isle of Wight, Norfolk, Suffolk and Wiltshire.

LONDON & SOUTH EAST DIVISION

Covers the counties of Kent, Surrey, East Sussex and West Sussex, and all London Boroughs

MIDLANDS DIVISION

Covers the counties of West Midlands, Leicestershire, Northamptonshire, Oxfordshire, Warwickshire, Derbyshire, Lincolnshire and Nottinghamshire.

YORKSHIRE & NORTH EAST DIVISION

Covers the counties and unitary authorities of Hartlepool, Middlesbrough, Redcar and Cleveland, Stockton-on-Tees, Durham, Hull, North Lincolnshire, North East Lincolnshire, East Riding, York, North Yorkshire, Northumberland, West Yorkshire, Tyne & Wear, and the metropolitan Boroughs of Barnsley, Doncaster, Rotherham and Sheffield.

NORTH WEST DIVISION

Covers the counties of Cheshire, Cumbria, Greater Manchester, Lancashire and Merseyside.

SCOTLAND

Covers all the Scottish unitary authorities and island councils.